Scotland's leading educational publishers

CW00555154

Active LEARNING
Curriculum for Excellence

S1
MATHEMATICS
Activity Workbook

Edward Mullan

CONTENTS

NUMBER, MEASURE AND MONEY

INTRODUCING NUMBERS

FRACTIONS, RATIO AND PROPORTION

TIME AND MEASUREMENT

PATTERN AND RELATIONSHIP

2

SHAPE, POSITION AND MOVEMENT

INFORMATION HANDLING

ANSWERS

INTRODUCTION

From the people who put the prices on the goods on the supermarket shelves to the people who put men in space, everyone uses mathematics.

From the people who draw the lines on the roads to the people who create avatars and computer graphics, everybody uses geometry.

From the people crossing roads to people crossing continents, everyone is engaged in measuring, whether it's time, distance, speed or area, volume and weight.

From the people playing board games to those playing the stock market, everyone is assessing risk and engaged in handling statistics.

Mathematics, with all its branches, touches almost every aspect of living.

If you want to participate fully in this modern world and become a responsible citizen then you must become familiar with the facets of Maths. 'Practice makes perfect', they say. If you want to become a successful learner then you'd better believe it.

The skills of mathematics are need in all other school subjects. Confidence in your Maths will help develop confidence in your abilities in other subjects and in yourself. Working with others and having confidence in yourself will help you to become an effective contributor, able to offer opinion, ideas and relevant input in team projects and class discussion.

The purpose of this book is to give you a skills check, to provide an opportunity to explore topics related to the subject at hand, to consider where the various branches of Maths bridge to other subjects, to provide a framework where you can plan to learn more efficiently and to get you to reflect on what has been learned, what should have been learned and how to rectify any difference between these two.

The contents of the book address the outcomes and experiences of the third level of the Curriculum for Excellence in Mathematics.

HOW TO USE THIS BOOK

This book should be used in conjunction with **Active Maths Course Notes**. The body of work at the third level has been arranged in 6 units and each unit has been further subdivided into topics (usually six)

You should attempt the materials covering all the topics in a unit in the corresponding sections of the **Active Maths Course Notes**. Using the exercises in this workbook will then act as a stimulus to revising the work.

Within each Unit there are Knowledge tips, points which should be particularly noted and real-life facts which hopefully will let you see the relevance of what you are learning.

After attempting the questions in a unit, your responses should be checked against the answers given at the back of the book. For these to be of value, you should not look at these answers until the questions have been attempted. When you come across questions which were answered wrongly you should attempt in the first instance to see where you went wrong yourself. This way you will learn better. If, after a bit of thought, you still can't see where you went wrong, ask for help.

Don't just ignore the gap in your knowledge that you've just found.

Within each unit there is the opportunity to try one or two activities. These will help you get a better grasp of the subject, add to the relevance of what you are learning, and let you see how it relates to real life and to other subjects in the school.

The activities are designed to get you to see how interesting Maths is. Follow up on leads and suggestions to do internet searches. A subject is only interesting if you make it interesting.

After the exercises there is an opportunity to look at your learning in a structured way. What should you have learned? A checklist is provided indicating the main points. You are then asked other questions designed to make you look at your own approach and the relation between the topics and your life and your other subjects. Different people will answer these questions in different ways. There is often more than one way of tackling a problem and other subjects, using the same Maths, might use it in a different way. You should try to note that and not get confused by the differing approaches.

When you have completed this workbook you should keep it as a revision resource.

INTRODUCING NUMBERS

QUESTIONS

TOP TIP

When rounding off, you first have to decide:
- Should I use the mathematical rule for rounding? (Q1)
- Should I round down no matter what? (Q2)
- Should I round up no matter what? (Q3)

1. ROUNDING

1. The population of Glasgow is 620 000. The population of Edinburgh is 678 070. Calculate the difference to the nearest ten thousand.

   ....

   ....

2. At the moment, 1 euro is worth £0·8856. To change pounds into euros we have to divide by 0·8856 and round. How many euros will you get for £100? (Remember it is a practical problem.)

   ....

   ....

3. For a room that is 2·5 m high, you can estimate how many rolls of wallpaper are needed when decorating. You should multiply the perimeter by 0·45 and round to the nearest necessary roll. Meg's room has a perimeter of 14 m. How many rolls of wallpaper should she buy?

   ....

   ....

2. USING NUMBERS

1. Galashiels to Edinburgh by bus costs £9·85 for a single journey; Edinburgh to Glasgow by train costs £18·60 for a return ticket. Calculate the total cost of the journey from Galashiels to Glasgow and back.

   ....

   ....

2. Find the product of 3·7 and 5·9 without using a calculator.

   ....

   ....

3. 'Give him an inch and he'll take an ell' was once a common phrase. An ell is an old-fashioned unit of length equal to 45 inches. 1 inch is 2·54 cm. How many centimetres make an ell?

   ....

   ....

4. A builder wants to build a flight of stairs. It should have 19 steps and the vertical height between the bottom and the top should be 323 cm. What is the rise of one step?

   ....

   ....

3. INTEGERS

1. Michael opened a new bank account. The first three entries look like this:

DATE	AMOUNT	BALANCE
2/4/09	£ 125.00	£ 125.00
9/4/09	-£ 32.00	....
16/4/09	-£ 25.00	....

   By adding the three amounts, calculate the final balance.

2. A person calculates his age by subtracting the year he was born from the year he is in. Augustus, the first emperor of Rome (and after whom the month of August is named) was born in 63 BC. How old was he in 14 AD, when he died? (Treat 63 BC as −63 and 14 AD as 14)

   ....

   ....

. A diver descends into the depths in steady steps. Height is measured in metres above sea level. Each minute the diver's height increases by -20 m.

(a) What does this really mean?

....

....

(b) The diver was 8 m above sea level. What is his height after 6 such steps?

....

....

REAL-LIFE FACT

Negative numbers are often used in science.

A ball rolling along a plane is timed. Distance from the start is positive going to the right and negative going to the left. Velocity is positive if the ball is moving to the right and negative if it is moving to the left. Time is positive if it is after the stopwatch has been started and negative if it is before.

---

4. MULTIPLES, FACTORS, PRIMES AND POWERS

. Eggs are packed either in boxes of 6 or boxes of 4. The farmer collected a number of eggs from around the farmyard. As it happens, they could be used to fill an exact number of either type of box. There were more than 30 but less than 40 eggs. How many eggs were collected?

....

....

. A rectangular floor is 525 cm by 1078 cm. A mosaic is to be laid on it marking off equal squares.

(a) List the factors of (i) 525 (ii) 1078

....

....

(b) What is the largest square that can be used to mark off the floor?

....

....

3. 1949 was a good year. EDSAC, the first stored-program computer, began working at Cambridge University ... and I was born. 1949 is a prime number. What is the prime number closest to your birth-year?

....

....

4. An ancient trader had a set of scales and a special set of weights. Using these he could weigh any amount of kilograms up to 121 kg. The lightest of the weights were:

and the diagrams shows how they are used to weigh 1kg to 5 kg.

(a) Work out the missing weights.

....

....

(b) What common idea links the values of the weights?

....

....

INTRODUCING NUMBERS

MAKE THE LINK

AN INTERDISCIPLINARY PROJECT

The following investigation will link the need for rounding with the handling of money and the use of computers. It will thus link Maths, Business Studies and Information Technology.

ROUNDING FUNCTIONS

... an investigation into rounding on a computer

In your IT class you will have learned about spreadsheets and how to use them to add, subtrac multiply and divide.

e.g. = A1 + A2 will add the contents of the cells A1 and A2.

   = A1 – A2 will subtract the content of cell A2 from that of A1.

   = A1 * A2 will multiply the contents of cells A2 and A1.

   = A1 / A2 will divide the contents of cell A1 by that of A2.

It is also useful to know the symbol '^', which means 'to the power of'.

e.g. = 2 ^ 4 means $2 \times 2 \times 2 \times 2 = 16$.

There are various functions in a spreadsheet that are useful when you want to round answers to calculations.

Task 1

CEILING and FLOOR

Suppose in A1 we have typed =31.2 + 423.52. What we get is 454·72.

In A2 type 1; in A3 type 2. Continue till A13 has 12.

In B2 type =CEILING(A1,A2). Fill down till B13.

CEILING	455	456	456	456	455	456	455	456	459	460	462	456
454.72	1	2	3	4	5	6	7	8	9	10	11	12

Each CEILING command takes the number in A1 (454·72) and rounds it up to the nearest multiple of the number in column A. Note that CEILING(A1,10) rounds up to the nearest 10. In a similar fashion, explore the purpose of FLOOR(*number, multiple*). How might it be used?

A farmer has a flock of 5000 hens. The average number of eggs laid per bird per day is 0·85. The eggs are boxed in sixes. How many boxes are needed?

Type in: =FLOOR(5000*0.85,6). The result is 4248. You'll need 4248 boxes.

Task 2

EVEN and ODD

Explore how =EVEN(*number*) behaves in a similar way. Can you think of uses for it? Do the same with =ODD(*number*). What is the effect of taking away 1 before you round?

e.g. with *number* = 67·4, what does = EVEN(67.4 − 1) and = ODD(67.4 − 1) give?

Task 3

ROUND behaves like a mixture of CEILING and FLOOR.

ROUND(*number*, *multiple*) … Explore its possibilities.

Task 4

ROUND

ROUNDDOWN

ROUNDUP

These three functions can be used when we want to fix the number of decimal places.
When working with money we usually want to round results to 2 decimal places.

Question: Share £685 amongst 6 people rounding up or down according to the *mathematical* rules.

Task 5

FUNC and INT

Both round positive numbers down to the nearest integer.
They behave differently with negative numbers. Investigate.

Read the following and then write a rule for rounding to any number of decimal places:

$10 = 10^1$ [10]

$100 = 10^2$ [10 × 10]

$1000 = 10^3$ [10 × 10 × 10]

To round to 1 decimal place: = INT(25/6*10^1 + 0.5)/10^1

To round to 2 decimal places: = INT(25/6*10^2 + 0.5)/10^2

To round to 3 decimal places: = INT(25/6*10^3 + 0.5)/10^3

TOP ACTIVITY TIP
Using '^' allows you to spot the pattern more easily.

INTRODUCING NUMBERS

MY PROGRESS

MY LEARNING CHECKLIST

1. *I can round a number using an appropriate degree of accuracy, having taken into account the context of the problem.* ◯

2. *I can use a variety of methods to solve number problems in familiar contexts, clearly communicating my processes and solutions.* ◯

3. *I can continue to recall number facts quickly and use them accurately when making calculations.* ◯

4. *I can use my understanding of numbers less than zero to solve simple problems in context.* ◯

5. *I have investigated strategies for identifying common multiples and common factors, explaining my ideas to others, and can apply my understanding to solve related problems.* ◯

6. *I can apply my understanding of factors to investigate and identify when a number is prime.* ◯

7. *Having explored the notation and vocabulary associated with whole number powers and the advantages of writing numbers in this form, I can evaluate powers of whole numbers mentally or using technology.* ◯

1. I can use these skills in everyday life by:

....

....

2. I can use these skills in other school subjects:

....

....

1. ....
....
....
....
....
....

2. ....
....
....
....
....
....

....
....
....
....
....
....

By gaining these number skills, I have been a successful learner in the following ways:

....
....
....
....
....
....

3. ....
....
....
....
....
....

4. ....
....
....
....
....
....

FRACTIONS, RATIO AND PROPORTION

QUESTIONS

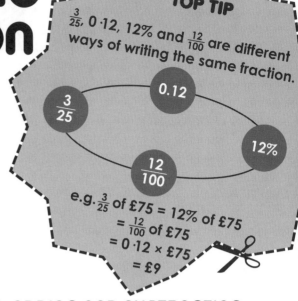

TOP TIP

$\frac{3}{25}$, 0·12, 12% and $\frac{12}{100}$ are different ways of writing the same fraction.

$\frac{3}{25}$ 0.12   12%

$\frac{12}{100}$

e.g. $\frac{3}{25}$ of £75 = 12% of £75

= $\frac{12}{100}$ of £75

= 0·12 × £75

= £9

1. FORMS OF FRACTIONS

1. Mike's brother is travelling the 68·4 km from Glasgow to Edinburgh. Mike gets a text message reading, 'On the way. 2 thirds of journey done.' How far is Mike's brother from Edinburgh?

    ....

    ....

    ....

2. Lemonade is sold in a bottle which holds $\frac{3}{4}$ litre. When $\frac{2}{5}$ of the contents are used, what fraction of a litre is left?
    (i.e. what is $\frac{3}{5} \times \frac{3}{4}$?)

    ....

    ....

    ....

3. A period of Maths lasts $\frac{3}{4}$ of an hour. The teacher estimates that a problem can be done in $\frac{1}{12}$ of an hour. How many similar problems can be done in a period?
    (i.e. What is $\frac{3}{4} \div \frac{1}{12}$?)

    ....

    ....

    ....

4. (a) Express $\frac{3}{8}$ as (i) a decimal fraction;
        (ii) a percentage.

    ....

    ....

    (b) Express 0·12 as (i) a common fraction;
        (ii) a percentage

    ....

    ....

    (c) Express 65% as (i) a decimal fraction;
        (ii) a common fraction.

    ....

    ....

    ....

2. ADDING AND SUBTRACTING FRACTIONS

1. The road sign below can be seen on a cycle track that joins two towns.
    (a) How far is it between Galashiels and Melrose?

    ....

    ....

    (b) How much closer to Galashiels is the sign

    ....

    ....

2. A sweets manufacturer sells fruit pastilles in packets of four flavours. In any packet of th. sweets, $\frac{1}{3}$ are orange flavoured, $\frac{1}{6}$ are lime, are lemon and the rest are blackcurrant. What fraction of a packet is blackcurrant?

    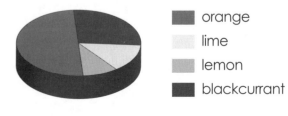

    orange
    lime
    lemon
    blackcurrant

    ....

    ....

12

Which of these sums is the odd one out?

(i) $\frac{1}{9} + \frac{1}{18}$ (ii) $\frac{1}{8} + \frac{1}{24}$ (iii) $\frac{1}{7} + \frac{1}{42}$ (iv) $\frac{1}{5} + \frac{1}{30}$

....

....

....

RATIO

The workings of a set of traffic lights were being studied. Over one hour it was found that the lights were red for 27 minutes. Express the fraction of the time the lights are red in its simplest form.

....

....

....

To make mayonnaise you should mix egg yoke, olive oil and vinegar in the ratio 2:9:1. A chef wishes to make 360 ml of mayonnaise. How much of each ingredient does he need?

....

....

....

A geologist will tell different types of igneous rocks apart by the ratio of silica to other minerals in the rock.

TYPE OF ROCK	SILICA CONTENT
Acid Rock	more than 60%
Basic Rock	45% – 60%
Ultrabasic Rock	less than 45%

A specimen is found to have a ratio of silica to other minerals of 4:1. How would this specimen be classified?

....

....

....

4. MONEY AND PERCENTAGES

1. A desktop computer was on sale for £400. It could be paid for in one go, or it could be bought for a deposit of 10% of the cash price plus 12 monthly instalments of £32·50.

   (a) How much is the deposit?

   ....

   ....

   (b) What is the total amount paid by the alternative method?

   ....

   ....

   (c) How much more expensive is the second method?

   ....

   ....

   ....

2. A bank offers interest at the rate of 2% per annum. Jenny left £5000 in the bank for 3 years. How much will be in the account after: (a) 1 year (b) 2 years (c) 3 years?

   ....

   ....

   ....

3. A credit card company charges interest at the rate of 1·27% per month. By considering how £100 will grow over 12 months, work out the APR being charged by the credit card company.

   ....

   ....

   ....

   ....

FRACTIONS, RATIO AND PROPORTION

MAKE THE LINK

AN INTERDISCIPLINARY PROJECT

The following investigation will link common fractions and ancient Egypt.
It will thus link Mathematics and History.

The Egyptians wrote down numbers like this:

1	2	3	4	5	6	7	8	9	10	100	1000

When they wanted to write fractions they used the symbol ⬭ above the number symbols.

For example, $\frac{1}{5}$ was written as 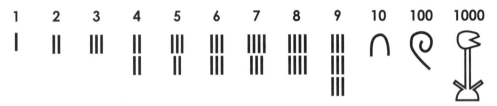 and $\frac{1}{20}$ as

Apart from two exceptions, $\frac{2}{3}$, $\frac{3}{4}$ all of their fractions had 1 as a numerator.

Task 1

How might they have written $\frac{5}{6}$?

(i) Check that $\frac{1}{7} + \frac{1}{42} = \frac{1}{8} + \frac{1}{24} = \frac{1}{9} + \frac{1}{18} = \frac{1}{10} + \frac{1}{15} = \frac{1}{6}$

(ii) So you have 4 ways of writing $\frac{1}{6}$ as the sum of two Egyptian fractions.

Which one can you adapt to let you express $\frac{5}{6}$ as Egyptian fractions?

Task 2

There is a simple set of steps which will allow you to express one Egyptian fraction as the sum c
two others. Take, for example, $\frac{1}{8}$:

(i) Square the denominator: 8 × 8 = 64

(ii) Write down all the factor pairs of the answer: (1, 64), (2, 32), (4, 16), (8, 8)

(iii) Add the original denominator, 8, to each number: (9, 72), (10, 40), (12, 24), (16, 16)

(iv) These are the denominators you need: $\frac{1}{9} + \frac{1}{72} = \frac{1}{10} + \frac{1}{40} = \frac{1}{12} + \frac{1}{24} = \frac{1}{16} + \frac{1}{16} = \frac{1}{8}$

The last pair of equal fractions were usually ignored as a possibility.

Use the same set of steps to write down the ways that $\frac{1}{10}$ can be expressed as a sum of two
Egyptian fractions.

Task 3

We can use the fact that $\frac{1}{8} = \frac{1}{9} + \frac{1}{72}$ to find a way of expressing $\frac{3}{8}$ as the sum of two Egyptian
fractions ... $\frac{3}{8} = \frac{3}{9} + \frac{3}{72} = \frac{1}{3} + \frac{1}{24}$

Express = $\frac{2}{8}, \frac{4}{8}, \frac{5}{8}, \frac{6}{8}$ as the sum of two Egyptian fractions.

$\frac{7}{8}$ cannot be written as the sum of two Egyptian fractions but it can be expressed as the sum of three. Find a way of doing it.

sk 4

 famous papyrus, the Rhind Papyrus, dates
 ack to 1650 BC. It contains a table which
 xpresses fractions of the form $\frac{2}{a}$, where a is an
 dd number between 5 and 101, as
 gyptian fractions.

 plore some of these expressions.

USEFUL RATIO

 the kitchen you will find lots of 'circular' objects;
 s, plates, breadboard, etc.

 Use a ruler or tape measure to measure:

(i) the distance across the 'circle' (the diameter)

(ii) the distance round the 'circle' (the circumference).

Put your findings in a table like the one shown below.

TOP ACTIVITY TIP

Look for formulae.
An odd number can always be written as $2a + 1$ where a is a whole number.
Consider the fractions $\frac{1}{(2a+1)(a+1)}$ and $\frac{1}{a+1}$.
e.g. Consider the odd number is 5. Then $2a + 1 = 5$ giving $a = 2$.
Then $a + 1 = 3$, $2a + 1 = 5$, and the two fraction are $\frac{1}{15}$ and $\frac{1}{3}$ which add to make $\frac{2}{5}$.

ITEM	DIAMETER (D cm)	CIRCUMFERENCE (C cm)	C : D
Bottle neck	2.5	7.9	
omato puree tube	5.5	17.3	
Side plate	18.5	58.1	
Tin of beans	7.5	23.6	
Bread board	25	78.5	
Grapefruit	8.5	26.7	
Dinner plate	26.5	83.3	

Use a spreadsheet and
draw a graph of
Diameter v
Circumference.

You should find that your
data and mine all lie on
the same straight line.

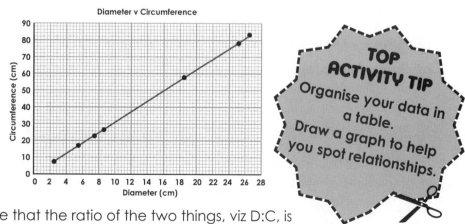

Diameter v Circumference

TOP ACTIVITY TIP

Organise your data in a table.
Draw a graph to help you spot relationships.

In mathematics, this is a clue that the ratio of the two things, viz D:C, is
the same for all pairs of figures.

In the column marked 'C:D', assuming the cell marked 'Item' is A1, type: =ROUND(B2/C2,2). This
should then give you the left-hand side of the ratio X. So that C:D = X:1. You should find that
each answer is the same. Of course, there will be some variation caused by errors in measuring.
Write a sentence stating the connection between the circumference and the diameter of a circle.

FRACTIONS, RATIO AND PROPORTION

MY PROGRESS

MY LEARNING CHECKLIST

1. *I can solve problems by carrying out calculations with a wide range of fractions, decimal fractions and percentages, using my answers to make comparisons and informed choices for real-life situations.*

2. *By applying my knowledge of equivalent fractions and common multiples, I can add and subtract commonly used fractions.*

3. *Having used practical, pictorial and written methods to develop my understanding, I can convert between whole or mixed numbers and fractions.*

4. *I can show how quantities that are related can be increased or decreased proportionally and apply this to solve problems in everyday contexts.*

5. *When considering how to spend my money, I can source, compare and contrast different contracts and services, discuss their advantages and disadvantages, and explain which offer best value to me.*

6. *I can budget effectively, making use of technology and other methods, to manage money and plan for future expenses*

1. I can use these skills in everyday life by:

....

....

2. I can use these skills in other school subjects:

....

....

16

FOUR CAPACITIES MIND MAP

1. ....
....
....
....
....

2. ....
....
....
....
....
....

....
....
....
....
....

By investigating
real-life
money issues,
I have learnt how
to be a responsible
citizen by:

....
....
....
....
....

3. ....
....
....
....
....
....

4. ....
....
....
....
....
....

TIME AND MEASUREMENT

QUESTIONS

1. TIME, DISTANCE, SPEED

Remember these:

1. A bus leaves the Galashiels bus station at 9:20. It arrives in the Edinburgh bus station at 10:35. This is a distance of 35 miles.
   (a) What is the time of the journey in
       (i) hours and minutes (ii) hours?

   ....

   ....

   (b) Calculate the average speed of the journey in miles per hour.

   ....

   ....

2. A car passes a speed camera. A second later a photograph is taken of it as it crosses road markings which measure the distance from the camera in metres. The legal speed limit for this particular stretch of road is 50 km/h. How far from the camera can the car get and still not be speeding?

   ....

   ....

3. Bryan lives in Glasgow. He has a bad cold and stayed in bed for 24 hours. As he lay there, the Earth made one complete turn and he travelled 22 583 km.
   (See the diagram)
   (a) How fast was Bryan moving just lying in bed?

   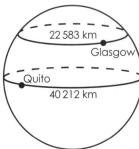

   ....

   ....

(b) He had a pen-pal in Quito, which is on the equator. The pen-pal also spent the day in bed. His journey round the earth is 40 212 km. How much faster is he travelling than Bryan?

....

....

2. MEASURING LENGTH

1. The BT tower in London is 189 m tall, including the aerial.
   A red telephone box is 254 cm tall.
   Jack is making a Trivia Section for a magazine and wants to give the height of the BT Tower in telephone boxes.
   How many telephone boxes high is it?

   ....

   ....

2. A car is 4·25 m long. A caravan, including the tow bar, is 534 cm long.
   What is the combined length of the car towing the caravan?

   ....

   ....

3. The cable for a vacuum cleaner is wound round two brackets. One complete loop is 138 cm. There are six such loops when the cable is completely wound. How long in metres is the cable?

   ....

   ....

. AREA

A factory wall is composed of a triangle and a rectangle as shown. The triangle has its long side facing south so that windows in the roof catch as much sun as possible.
Calculate the area of

(a) the triangle

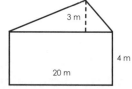

....

(b) the rectangle

....

(c) the total area of the side

....

When the radio of the Salty Sally went dead, the air–sea rescue set up a search area of radius 10 km around its last known position. Calculate the area of this circle.

....

....

The archway is made up of a semicircle and a rectangle. The important sizes are given.
Calculate the area of the opening

....

....

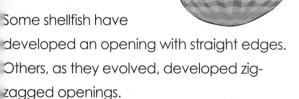
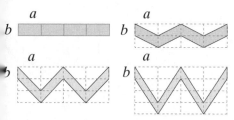
4. VOLUME

1. Find the volume of each solid:

(a) cuboid   (b) prism   (c) pyramid.

length = 7 cm
height = 3 cm   area of base = 5 cm²   area of base = 12 cm²
width = 2 cm   height = 4 cm   height = 5 cm

....

....

....

....

2. What is the volume of each container?

(a) soap   (b) furniture   (c) cleaner.
   powder   polish

  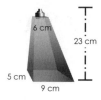

....

....

....

....

Bottle (c) is a prism with a base which is a trapezium and a 'height' of 5 cm.

3. The volume of a sphere is calculated using: $V = \frac{4}{3}\pi r^3$.
From the centre of the Earth to the outer mantle is 6·450 units.

(a) Calculate the volume of this sphere.

....

....

....

(b) From the centre of the Earth to the surface is 6·490 units. Calculate the volume of the Earth's crust.

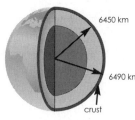

....

....

....

TIME AND MEASUREMENT

MAKE THE LINK

INTERDISCIPLINARY PROJECT

The following investigation requires the making of pieces of a puzzle to a fair degree of precision. It will link Mathematics (volume and 3D shapes) and Technical Studies.

Essentially the puzzle deals with areas but the fun aspect and surprise is stronger when considering volumes.

You need five trapezia based on the dissection of a 3 by 3 grid as shown, and a box into which they fit snugly.

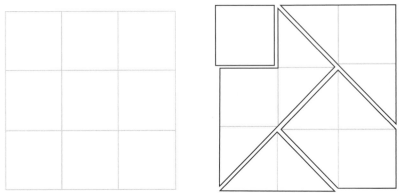

You can make them from wood or from the following nets. These are possibly too small to work with. Either photo-enlarge on a copier or re-draw them. The grey panels are glueing tabs.

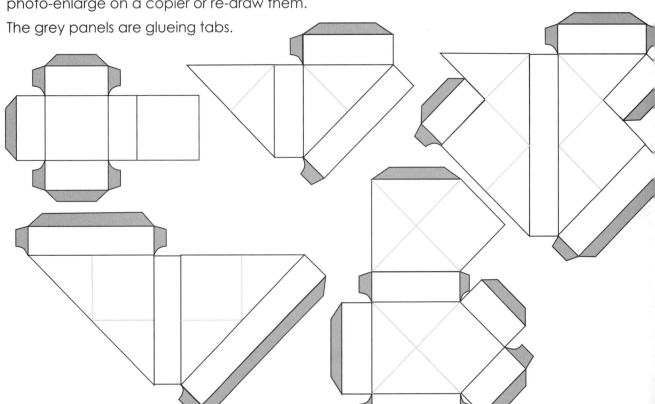

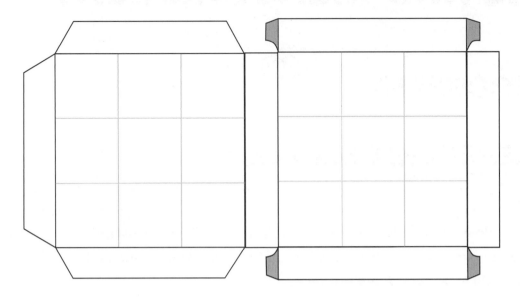

he pieces can be dressed up as packets or presents and the box can be decorated as a
uitcase with labels and a handle.

Give your friend the suitcase and four of the pieces, all but the 'square'.
sk him or her to pack the suitcase. After a few minutes he or she will no doubt come up with
his answer:

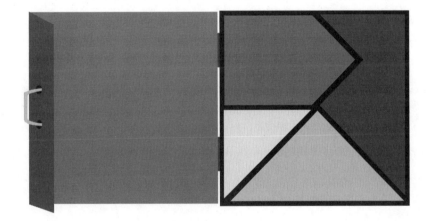

he four pieces fit quite nicely into the box. While your friend is feeling pleased with the packing
ou can produce the 'square' and say, 'Oops. I forgot this piece. It belongs in the suitcase too.'
our friend will believe it's impossible, rather than believe the small gaps between the 4 pieces
dd up to the same volume as the 'square' piece.

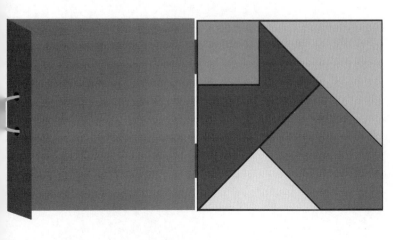

TOP ACTIVITY TIP
When things are hard to visualise, make a model.

TIME AND MEASUREMENT

MY PROGRESS

MY LEARNING CHECKLIST

1. *Using simple time periods, I can work out how long a journey will take, the speed travelled at or distance covered, using my knowledge of the link between time, speed and distance.* ◯

2. *I can solve practical problems by applying my knowledge of measure, choosing the appropriate units and degree of accuracy for the task and using a formula to calculate area or volume when required.* ◯

3. *Having investigated different routes to a solution, I can find the area of compound 2D shapes and the volume of compound 3D objects, applying my knowledge to solve practical problems.* ◯

1. I can use these skills in everyday life by:

    ....

    ....

2. I can use these skills in other school subjects:

    ....

    ....

FOUR CAPACITIES MIND MAP

1. ....
....
....
....
....
....

2. ....
....
....
....
....
....

....
....
....
....
....
....

The teamwork and paired activities that I have taken part in during Maths class have helped me to become an effective contributor by:

....
....
....
....
....
....

3. ....
....
....
....
....
....

4. ....
....
....
....
....

PATTERN AND RELATIONSHIP

QUESTIONS

TOP TIP
When looking for patterns:
• examine the difference between terms.
• consider where the sequence starts.

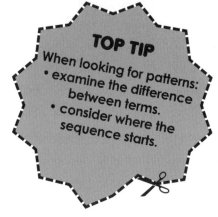

1. PATTERN

1. Write down the first four terms of the sequences which have an nth term formula:

(a) $3n + 1$

....

(b) $100 - 2n$

....

(c) $6n - 7$

....

2. Write down a formula for the nth term of the sequence

(a) 1, 5, 9, 13, ...

....

(b) 7, 16, 25, 34, ...

....

(c) 99, 93, 87, 81, ...

....

3. The Romans used to decorate their floors with mosaics. The borders of these mosaics were called 'key' patterns. Each pattern was built up of a left-hand end, a right-hand end and as many middle bits as required.

 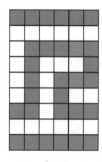 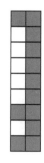

... Here is a border with 6 middle bits.

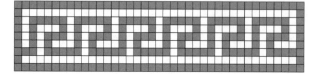

The number of small red tiles needed to make a strip with n middle bits is $9 + 30n + 12$

(a) Explain the formula.

....

....

(b) Write down the number of red tiles needed for a border with 1, 2, 3, 4, 5 middle bits.

....

....

2. EXPRESSIONS

1. The class magazine used 6 sheets of paper. After all the magazines had been made, there were 8 sheets of paper left from a packet of paper. If there were x magazines made, write an expression for the number of sheets in a packet.

....

....

2. A batch of eggs was boxed in sixes and in dozens. Once the batching was done there were 5 eggs left over. If there were x boxes of 6 and y boxes of 12, write an expression for the number of eggs in a batch.

....

....

3. Helen bought a washing machine on hire purchase. She made a deposit of £50 and made x equal instalments. Let the total cost of the machine be £350. Find an expression for:

(a) the size of an instalment

....

(b) how much she still has to pay after 5 instalments.

....

EQUATIONS

Solve each equation

(a) $4x + 7 = 39$

....

....

(b) $10k - 3 = 87$

....

....

(c) $80 - 6x = 14$

....

....

. In the last census it was found that the population of Wales was double that of Northern Ireland, that the population of Scotland was 3 times that of Northern Ireland and that the population of England was 29 times bigger than that of Northern Ireland. The population of the whole UK was 58 800 000

(a) Form an equation letting x represent the population of Northern Ireland.

....

....

(b) Solve it to find the population of Northern Ireland.

....

....

(c) Calculate the population of each part of the UK.

....

....

. Jamie's sister is 8 years old. He asks their father what his age is. His father tells them he's double their combined age and just as old as their mother. Jamie asks their mother her age and she says she's three times as old as him plus half as old as his sister.

(a) Let x years be Jamie's age. Form an equation using the clues.

....

....

(b) Solve it to find everybody's age.

....

....

4. FORMULAE

1. The density of a material is often used to help identify the material. It is calculated from the formula $D = \frac{m}{v}$ where D is the density in grams per cm³, m is the mass in grams and v is the volume in millilitres.
   A scientist had 154 ml of a metal which weighted 1386 g.
   Calculate the density of the material and decide whether it is gold (19·3 g/cm³), copper (9·0 g/cm³) or silver (10·5 g/cm³).

   ....

   ....

2. A regular polygon has equal sides and equal angles. The size of each angle, A, can be calculated using the formula
   $$A = \frac{180(n - 2)}{n}$$
   where n is the number of sides.
   Complete the table:

NUMBER OF SIDES (n)	3	4	5	6	10
SIZE OF ANGLE ($A°$)					

PATTERN AND RELATIONSHIP

MAKE THE LINK

AN INTERDISCIPLINARY PROJECT

The following gives you a way of using expressions, substitution and formulae to help you work out the date of Easter for any year. This can be done on a spreadsheet and will link Maths, Religious Studies, History, Computing and Science (Astronomy).

Historical Note

Easter Sunday was set by the Council of Nicaea in 325 AD as the Sunday *after* the full moon *on or after* the Spring Equinox. The earliest it could be is the 22nd March and the latest 25th April.

The table below should be worked out by forming expressions and performing whole number divisions … divisions which yield a whole number answer (the quotient) and a remainder.

EXPRESSION	VALUE	DIVIDE BY	QUOTIENT	REMAINDER
Year		100	a	b
$5a + b$		19	c	d
$3a + 75$		4	e	f
$8a + 88$		25	g	h
$19d + e - g$		30	i	j
$d + 11j$		319	k	l
$300 - 60f + b$		4	m	n
$2m - n - j + k$		7	p	q
$j - k + q + 110$		30	r	s
$s + 5 - r$		32	t	u

ere 2011 has been computed:

EXPRESSION	VALUE	DIVIDE BY	ANSWER		REMAINDER	
Year	<u>2011</u>	100	20	a	11	b
5a + b	111	19	5	c	16	d
3a + 75	135	4	33	e	3	f
3a + 88	248	25	9	g	23	h
19d + e − g	328	30	10	i	28	j
d + 11j	324	319	1	k	5	l
300 − 60f + b	131	<u>4</u>	32	m	3	n
2m − n − j + k	34	7	4	p	6	q
− k + q + 110	143	30	4	r	23	s
+ 5 − r	24	32	0	t	<u>24</u>	u
EASTER IS THE 24TH OF APRIL						

e underlined numbers give the date of Easter Sunday:

4/4/2011

ou can programme a spreadsheet to do this job.
ssume the word 'Expression' is in cell A1.
pe in all the bits you see in the top table.

 B2 type the year in which you are interested.

 B3 type: = 5*D2 + F2

 the rest of the B column type the formula that
 orresponds with the expressions in the A column.

 D2 type: = QUOTIENT(B2,C2) ... to calculate
 e quotient.

 this down for the rest of the table.

 F2 type: = B2 − C2*D2 ... to calculate the remainder.

 this down for the rest of the table.

 B12 type: = CONCATENATE ("Easter is the ",F11,"th of ", CHOOSE (D10 − 2,"March","April"))
 is declares the answer.

 hange the year in B2 and the sheet will automatically work out Easter Sunday for that year.

TOP ACTIVITY TIP

Spreadsheets are useful to let you see how formulae behave as variables change. Patterns can be spotted easily where before it might have taken a lot of number-crunching to achieve similar results.
For instance, there are patterns in Easter dates ... look for cycles of 11 years.
In 2013 the date of Easter is a palindrome. What's that?

PATTERN AND RELATIONSHIP

MY PROGRESS

MY LEARNING CHECKLIST

1. *Having explored number sequences, I can establish the set of numbers generated by a given rule and determine a rule for a given sequence, expressing it using appropriate notation.* ○

2. *I can collect like algebraic terms, simplify expressions and evaluate using substitution.* ○

3. *Having discussed ways to express problems or statements using mathematical language, I can construct and use appropriate methods to solve a range of simple equations.* ○

4. *I can create and evaluate a simple formula representing information contained in a diagram, problem or statement.* ○

1. I can use these skills in everyday life by:

....

....

2. I can use these skills in other school subjects:

....

....

1. ....
....
....
....
....
....

....
....
....
....
....
....

2. ....
....
....
....
....
....

Gaining these number skills has increased my confidence by:

....
....
....
....
....
....

3. ....
....
....
....
....
....

4. ....
....
....
....
....

SHAPE, POSITION AND MOVEMEN

QUESTIONS

1. DRAWING TRIANGLES

1. Draw a triangle with sides 4 cm, 5 cm
   and 7 cm.
   You'll need a pair of compasses.
   (a) Measure the size of each angle.

   ....

   ....

   (b) Complete the sentence, 'The biggest
       angle is opposite ...'

   ....

   ....

2. A triangle has vertices A, B and C.
   AB = 6 cm, AC = 8 cm, ∠BAC = 50°.
   (a) Draw △ ABC.

   ....

   ....

   (b) What is the length of the side BC?

   ....

   ....

3. Neil takes a loop of rope and pegs it out to
   form a triangle.
   Below is a sketch of the triangle formed.

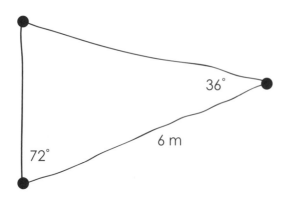

   (a) Make an accurate scale drawing of
       the triangle.

   ....

   ....

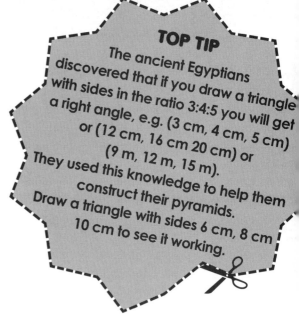

TOP TIP
The ancient Egyptians discovered that if you draw a triangle with sides in the ratio 3:4:5 you will get a right angle, e.g. (3 cm, 4 cm, 5 cm) or (12 cm, 16 cm 20 cm) or (9 m, 12 m, 15 m).
They used this knowledge to help them construct their pyramids.
Draw a triangle with sides 6 cm, 8 cm 10 cm to see it working.

   (b) What is the total length of the rope?

   ....

   ....

2. ANGLES

1. Calculate the size of as many angles as
   you can in this drawing of a rectangle.
   (Note that two lines are parallel.)

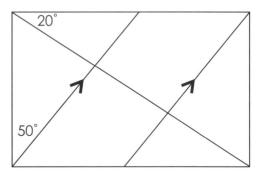

2. In this diagram you can find three
   parallelograms and four triangles.

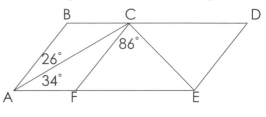

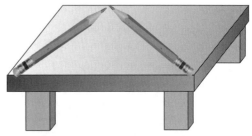

(a) Find the size of each angle in triangle CFE.

....

....

(b) Prove AC = CE.

....

....

(c) Illusion: Which pencil is longer?

....

....

A scaffold is built on a slope. Two vertical struts hold up a horizontal platform. The assembly is braced by two diagonals.

Show that triangle ABE is not isosceles. (Hint: imagine it is isosceles and find as many angles as possible.)

....

....

3. MAPS AND PLANS

1. (a) A map has a scale so that 1 cm represents 20 km. What is the actual distance between two spots which are 3·4 cm apart on the map?

....

....

(b) Another map is such that two towns which are actually 51 km apart are represented by dots which are 3·4 cm apart. What is the scale of the map?

....

....

2. On this map of Loch Lomond 1cm represents 5 km.

(a) Measure the bearing of
(i) Balloch from Ardlui

....

(ii) Cardross from Balloch

....

(b) Calculate the distance between Ardlui and...
(i) Cardross

....

....

(ii) Balloch

....

....

3. The Channel tunnel links Folkestone in England to Coquelles in France. The bearing of Coquelles from Folkestone is 112°. What is the bearing of Folkestone from Coquelles?

....

....

....

REAL-LIFE FACT

Surveyors and map-makers make use of triangles to help them fix the positions of points.

A starting line, AB is accurately measured. The angles ∠CAB and ∠CBA can be measured from A and B using a measuring instrument called a theodolite.

This then pinpoints C. The angles ∠DCB and ∠DBC can then be measured and D can be pinpointed.

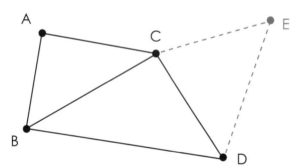

This can be continued as long as necessary to accurately position all points on the map with reference to the initial two points.
This is known as triangulation. The points are called triangulation points and since they have to be seen clearly, they are often placed on top of hills and mountains and marked by concrete blocks.

4. COORDINATES

1. A(2, 2), B(0, 5), C(6, 9) and D are the vertices of a rectangle.

    (a) Draw the rectangle on the grid.

    ....

    (b) Give the coordinates of D.

    ....

    (c) Where do the diagonals cross?

    ....

    (d) A congruent rectangle, EFGH, is drawn where E(4, 3) and G(12, 4) are the end of one diagonal.
    Draw the rectangle and give the coordinates of the vertices.

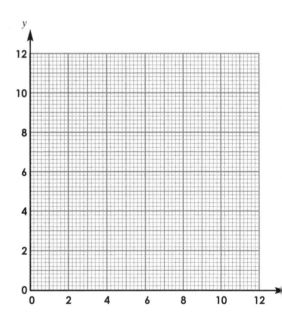

2. Archaeologists have found some post holes of a medieval round-house. Here are their coordinates:

    (0, 6), (1, 9), (2, 10), (5, 11), (8, 10), (9, 9), (10, 6), (9, 3), (8, 2), (5, 1), (2, 2), (1, 3).

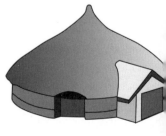

32

(a) On the grid, plot the points and give the coordinates of the centre of the round-house.

(b) What is the diameter of the round house if each square of the grid is a metre?

....

....

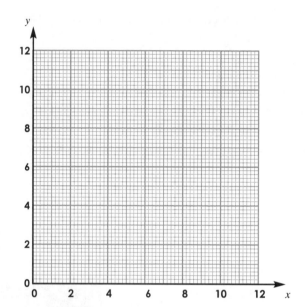

2. The kite ABCD has sides AB = 5 cm and CD = 8 cm.

   $\angle ADB = 36°$, $\angle DBC = 70°$.

   (a) Make a sketch of the kite.

33

SYMMETRY

Make a sketch of and draw the axes of symmetry of:

(a) a rectangle

(b) a rhombus

(c) a kite

(b) Calculate:

   (i) the size of each angle of the kite

   (ii) the perimeter of the kite

....

....

....

3. Reflect the right hand part of the grid into the mirror to reveal an appropriate word.

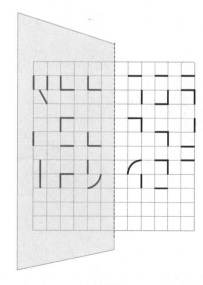

MAKE THE LINK

AN INTERDISCIPLINARY PROJECT

The following gives you a way of using exploring transformations with the aid of a computer. The drawing tools of a basic Word package are all that is required.

You can use it to investigate the tiling properties of various shapes in particular and patterns in space in general.

This will link Maths, Art, Religious Studies (Moorish Patterns), History and Computing.

DRAWING TILES

Open a Word document and using the View menu, make sure the drawing tools are available
Use the Freeform tool to draw a triangle.
Fill the triangle with a suitable colour, say, red, and duplicate it 6 times.
Use the selection tool to select all 6 triangles:
duplicate this 6 times. Choose a different fill colour, blue.
Use the drawing tools to 'Flip Vertically' and then 'Flip Horizontally'
… so you now have 6 red tiles and 6 blue, which are upside down.

Freeform

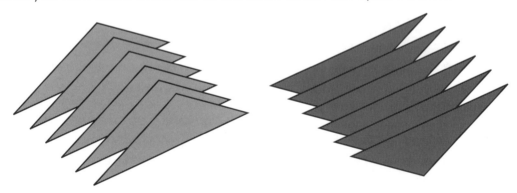

In the drawing tools, set the grid to 'snap to other objects'.

Drag a red tile to the centre of the page:

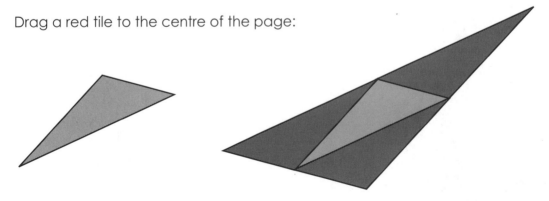

...urround it by 3 blues;

...ow place a red tile against each blue edge;

...en a blue against each red edge; and so on. Duplicate tiles as you need them.

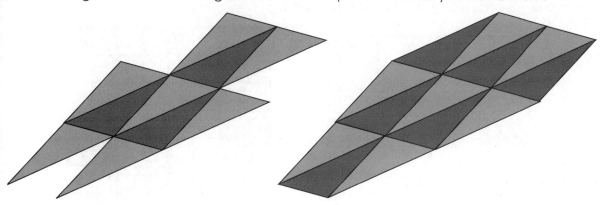

...his method can be used on any triangle ... any set of congruent triangles will tile.

...hat does that tell you about the angles of a triangle?

...xplore the same idea with quadrilaterals:

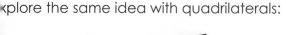
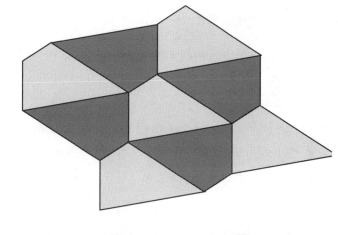

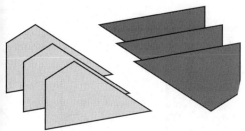

...works with this irregular quadrilateral;

...works with this V-kite.

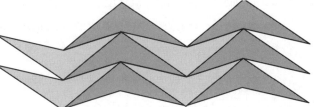

...hat does that tell you about the angles of a quadrilateral?

...istorical Note

...amic art has, as a tradition, always avoided representing living things ... avoiding imitating

...od's work. As a result they became highly skilled in producing abstract patterns in their art

...nd tilings. Explore 'Islamic Art' on the web.

...ook for repeat patterns and symmetry.

SIMPLE SYMMETRY

Make a simple tiling of a square, say 4 by 4.

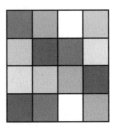

Colour each square randomly.
Use the drawing tools to 'Group' the squares together.
Duplicate the tiling and flip it horizontally.
Group the two tilings together to make an 8 by 4 grid.

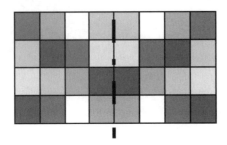

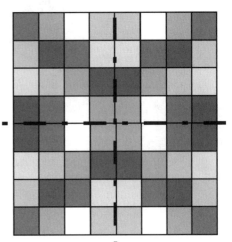

Duplicate this grid and flip vertically.
Place duplicate under the original and Group
to make an 8 by 8 grid with two axes of symmetry.

Experiment with colours and grid-size.

36

MAKING FLOWERS

A buttercup has 5 axes of symmetry.
$360 \div 5 = 72$

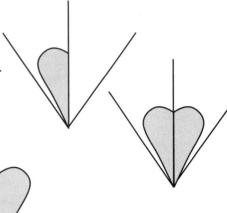

Draw a vertical line. Duplicate and rotate through 36° (72÷2).
Duplicate the rotated line and flip horizontally.
Place all three lines touching at the bottom.
These will act as guide lines.

Draw half a petal using the curve tool. Fill it yellow.
Duplicate and flip horizontally, place beside the
original and group to make one symmetrical petal.
You can delete the guidelines now.

Duplicate and rotate through 72°.
Duplicate and rotate through 144° (2 x 72).
Duplicate and rotate through 216° (3 x 72).
Duplicate and rotate through 288° (4 x 72).
Position the 5 petals tip-to-tip (you may need to switch off the 'Snap' to do this).

Make a small circle; colour it yellow then select 'Fill effects' > 'Pattern' > and select the 'Large confetti' pattern. Place this circle over the centre of the flower. and group.

Work out the rotation angles for other flowers and experiment in making bouquets.

TOP ACTIVITY TIP
Experimentation leads to discovery.
Don't be frightened of experimentation.

SHAPE, POSITION AND MOVEMEN

MY PROGRESS

MY LEARNING CHECKLIST

1. *Having investigated a range of methods, I can accurately draw 2D shapes using appropriate mathematical instruments and methods.* ◯

2. *I can name angles and find their sizes using my knowledge of the properties of a range of 2D shapes and the angle properties associated with intersecting and parallel lines.* ◯

3. *Having investigated navigation in the world, I can apply my understanding of bearings and scale to interpret maps and plans and create accurate plans, and scale drawings of routes and journeys.* ◯

4. *I can apply my understanding of scale when enlarging or reducing pictures and shapes, using different methods, including technology* ◯

5. *I can use my knowledge of the coordinate system to plot and describe the location of a point on a grid.* ◯

6. *I can illustrate the lines of symmetry for a range of 2D shapes and apply my understanding to create and complete symmetrical pictures and patterns.* ◯

1. I can use these skills in every-day life by:

....

....

2. I can use these skills in other school subjects:

....

....

1. ....
....
....
....
....
....

....
....
....
....
....
....

2. ....
....
....
....
....
....

Successfully learning these problem-solving skills will help me think creatively and independently by:

....
....
....
....
....

3. ....
....
....
....
....
....

4. ....
....
....
....
....
....

INFORMATION HANDLING

QUESTIONS

1. DATA HANDLING

1. Calculate the mean of each set of data correct to 1 decimal place.
    (a) 3 cm, 6 cm, 4 cm, 8 cm, 12 cm

    ....
    ....

    (b) 1·5 sec, 2·7 sec, 3·1 sec, 2·9 sec, 2·1 sec, 3·5 sec

    ....
    ....

2. A market research survey into the colour of packaging on supermarket shelves took place. Packets were selected at random and the main colour noted.
    The table summarises the findings.

COLOUR	RED	ORANGE	YELLOW	GREEN	BLUE
Number of packets	12	16	28	22	22

    (a) State the (i) most (ii) least popular colour.

    ....
    ....

    (b) Draw a bar chart to illustrate the data.

    (c) How big was the sample?

    ....
    ....

(d) What fraction of the sample was orange? Express this in its simplest form.

....
....
....
....

3. As a river slows down, the pebbles and san that are being carried fall down to the river bed. A geologist measures the size of these pebbles at different depths in the bed.

DEPTH (cm)	1	2	3	4	5	6	7	8	9	1
PEBBLE SIZE (mm)	4	14	19	22	25	32	34	45	46	5

    (a) Make a graph of depth against pebble size.

    (b) What is the relationship between pebble size and depth?

    ....
    ....

2. PROBABILITY

1. State the probability that when two odd numbers are chosen at random
    (a) their product will be even

    ....
    ....

    (b) their sum will be even

    ....
    ....

Seven cards from a pack of 52 have already been turned over.

(a) What is the probability that the next one to be turned will be a

(i) king?

....

(ii) 6

....

(b) What is more likely:
  (i) it will be a heart?
  (ii) it will be a spade?

....

....

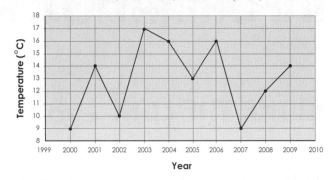

Temperature in Ayton June 5th (Noon)

In Ayton village they hold a gala day on June 5th each year.

The table and chart give the mid-day temperatures over the past 10 years.

(a) State the minimum and maximum temperature recorded.

....

....

(b) Calculate the average temperature.

....

....

(c) What is the probability that this year it will be warmer than average at Ayton Gala?

....

....

....

41

TOP TIP

The idea behind a survey is that the sample will reflect the population. The bigger the sample, the more closely it will behave like the population. The difference between what you find and what is actually the case is called the sampling error. Don't read too much into findings from small-sample surveys. The context is also important. The findings from the river-bed survey on page 38 will only be sound for that neighbourhood of the river. It may not be true when the water is running rapidly.

YEAR	TEMP (c°)
2000	9
2001	14
2002	10
2003	17
2004	16
2005	13
2006	16
2007	9
2008	12
2009	14

TOP TIP

Probability theory was developed by two famous French mathematicians, Fermat and Pascal. They developed it while trying to sort out a gambling dispute ... Two players are involved in a game. Each has put 32 coins in the 'pot'. For winning a round, a player gets a point. For being the first to get 3 points a player gets the pot. However, the game was interrupted when one player had 2 points and the other had 1. How should the pot be shared out? Since then probability theory has found many uses in such diverse fields as weather forecasting, life insurance and risk assessment, as well as being used to advise in stock control.

INFORMATION HANDLING

MAKE THE LINK

The following gives you a way of using statistics and probability to examine codes and the logic behind cracking them.

You can use the same findings to examine the efficiency of Morse Code (why, for example, is the letter E represented by a single dot?) ... or the logic behind the scoring in Scrabble (why should using an E get you 1 point while using a Z gets you 10 points?). Would the scoring in the French version be the same as that in the English version?

This will link Maths, History, English and Languages.

CODES AND SCRABBLE

While Mary, Queen of Scots was held captive by Elizabeth I, she plotted with Anthony Babington to escape, to assassinate Elizabeth and to take the throne. They communicated by letters written in code. These were intercepted and the code was broken. Mary was tried and executed in 1587.

Her code can now be found on the internet ... Google 'Mary Queen of Scots Cipher'.
But how do you crack these codes?

42

Task 1

Pick any book and select a page at random.
Pick a passage of about 20 lines and do a count of each letter. You will find the use of tally marks helps.

Task 2

Divide each frequency by the total number of letters counted.
This will give an estimate of the probability of each letter.
Compare your findings with this table. They shouldn't differ too much.

A	B	C	D	E	F	G	H	I
0.08	0.02	0.03	0.04	0.13	0.02	0.02	0.06	0.07
J	**K**	**L**	**M**	**N**	**O**	**P**	**Q**	**R**
0.002	0.008	0.04	0.02	0.07	0.08	0.02	0.001	0.06
S	**T**	**U**	**V**	**W**	**X**	**Y**	**Z**	
0.06	0.09	0.03	0.01	0.02	0.002	0.02	0.001	

The simplest type of code is called a Caesar Shift.

This is named after Julius Caesar, who is supposed to have used it.

The alphabet is laid out in a line and is written out again underneath it, shifted by a few letters:

Alphabet:	A B C D E F G H I J K L M N O P Q R S T U V W X Y Z
Code:	K L M N O P Q R S T U V W X Y Z A B C D E F G H I J

The message 'REMEMBER THE FIFTH OF NOVEMBER' becomes 'BOWOWLOB DRO PSPDR YP XYFOWLOB'.

How would you de-code it?

Well, doing a count of the letters in the coded message lets you see that O is the letter which occurs the most. Your previous survey has let you see that E is normally the most common letter. Perhaps O stands for E.

Write out the alphabet and underneath it write it out again with E under O.

This is then the key to use for decoding.

Code:	A B C D E F G H I J K L M N O P Q R S T U V W X Y Z
Alphabet:	Q R S T U V W X Y Z A B C D E F G H I J K L M N O P

Can you find the key for this message?

'NZQMVL QV VMML QA I NZQMVL QVLMML'

Historical Note

The need to crack codes accelerated the development of the computer in WWII.

Google 'Bletchley Park'.

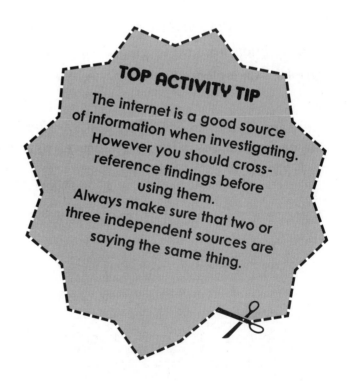

TOP ACTIVITY TIP

The internet is a good source of information when investigating. However you should cross-reference findings before using them. Always make sure that two or three independent sources are saying the same thing.

43

INFORMATION HANDLING

MY PROGRESS

MY LEARNING CHECKLIST

1. *I can work collaboratively, making appropriate use of technology, to source information presented in a range of ways, interpret what it conveys and discuss whether I believe the information to be robust, vague or misleading.*

2. *When analysing information or collecting data of my own, I can use my understanding of how bias may arise and how sample size can affect precision, to ensure that the data allows for fair conclusions to be drawn.*

3. *I can display data in a clear way using a suitable scale, by choosing appropriately from an extended range of tables, charts, diagrams and graphs, making effective use of technology.*

4. *I can find the probability of a simple event happening and explain why the consequences of the event, as well as its probability, should be considered when making choices.*

1. I can use these skills in every-day life by:

....

....

2. I can use these skills in other school subjects:

....

....

1. ....
....
....
....
....
....

....
....
....
....
....
....

2. ....
....
....
....
....
....

Learning about codes has helped me to understand communication better by:

....
....
....
....
....

3. ....
....
....
....
....
....

4. ....
....
....
....
....
....

ANSWERS
NUMBER, MEASURE AND MONEY

INTRODUCING NUMBERS

1. **Rounding**
   1. 60 000
   2. 112 euros (must round down)
   3. 7 rolls (must round up)

2. **Using numbers**
   1. £38·30
   2. 21·83
   3. 114·3
   4. 17 cm

3. **Integers**
   1. £68
   2. $14 - (-63) = 77$
   3. (a) He goes *down* 20 m.   (b) −112 m

4. **Multiples, factors, primes and powers**
   1. 36
   2. (a) (i) 1, 3, 5, 7, 15, 21, 25, 35, 75, 105, 175, 525
          (ii) 1, 2, 7, 11, 14, 22, 49, 77, 98, 154, 539, 1078
      (b) 7 m
   3. The following years are primes: 1949, 1951, 1973, 1979, 1987, 1993, 1997, 1999, 2003, 2011, 2017, 2027, 2029, 2039, 2053, 2063
   4. (a) 1, 3, 9, 27, 81
      (b) They are powers of three.

FRACTIONS, RATIO AND PROPORTION

1. **Forms of fractions**
   1. 22·8 km
   2. $\frac{9}{20}$ litre
   3. 9 problems
   4. (a) (i) 0·375   (ii) 37·5%
      (b) (i) $\frac{12}{100} = \frac{3}{25}$ (ii) 12%
      (c) (i) 0·65   (ii) $\frac{65}{100} = \frac{13}{20}$

2. **Adding and subtracting fractions**
   1. (a) $3\frac{3}{4}$ miles   (b) $1\frac{1}{4}$ miles
   2. $\frac{7}{18}$
   3. (iv) ... all others equal $\frac{1}{6}$

3. **Ratio**
   1. $\frac{27}{60} = \frac{9}{20}$
   2. 60 ml eggs; 270 ml oil; 30 ml vinegar

3. $\frac{4}{5} = 80\%$ ... acid

4. **Money and percentages**
   1. (a) £40   (b) £430   (c) £30
   2. (a) £5100   (b) £5202   (c) £5306·04
   3. 16·35%

TIME AND MEASUREMENT

1. **Time, distance, speed**
   1. (a) (i) 1h 15 m
          (ii) 1·25h
      (b) 28 m/h
   2. $13\frac{8}{9} = 13.89$ m (to 2 d.p.)
   3. (a) 941 km/h (b) 734·5 km/h faster.

2. **Measuring length**
   1. 74 telephone boxes
   2. 9·59 m
   3. 8·28 m

3. **Area**
   1. (a) 30 m²   (b) 80 m²   (c) 110 m²
   2. 314 km²
   3. 75·2 m²

4. **Volume**
   1. (a) 42 m³   (b) 20 cm³   (c) 20 cm³
   2. (a) 1680 cm³ (b) 491 cm³   (c) 862·5 cr
   3. (a) 1124 units³
      (b) 1145 units³ − 1124 units³ = 21 units³

PATTERN AND RELATIONSHIP

1. **Pattern**
   1. (a) 4, 7, 10, 13
      (b) 98, 96, 94, 92
      (c) −1, 5, 11, 17
   2. (a) $4n - 3$ (b) $9n - 2$ (c) $105 - 6n$
   3. (a) 9 reds on left, 12 reds on right, and 30 reds for each of n middles.
      (b) 51, 81, 111, 141, 171

2. **Expressions**
   1. $6x + 8$
   2. $6x + 12y + 5$
   3. (a) $300 \div x$
      (b) $300 - (1500/x)$

46

Equations

1. (a) $4x + 7 = 39 \Rightarrow 4x = 32 \Rightarrow x = 8$

   (b) $10k - 3 = 87 \Rightarrow 10k = 90 \Rightarrow k = 9$

   (c) $80 - 6x = 14 \Rightarrow 6x = 66 \Rightarrow x = 11$

2. (a) $x + 2x + 3x + 29x = 58\ 800\ 000$

   (b) $35x = 58\ 800\ 000 \Rightarrow x = 1\ 680\ 000$

   (c) Wales = 3 360 000; Scotland = 5 040 000;

   England = 48 720 000

3. (a) Father = mother $\Rightarrow x + 8 + x + 8 = 3x + 4$

   (b) $2x + 16 = 3x + 4 \Rightarrow x = 12$

   Jamie is 12, sister is 8, father and mother

   are both 40.

Formulae

1. $1386 \div 154 = 9$. Copper.

2.

Number of sides (n)	3	4	5	6	10
Size of angle $(A°)$	60	90	108	120	144

SHAPE, POSITION AND MOVEMENT

Drawing triangles

1. (a) Your drawing will be right if your angles
   are close to 44°, 101°, 35°

   (b) 'The biggest angle is opposite the
   biggest side.'

2. (a) Your drawing will be right if BC is about
   6 cm.

   (b) BC is about 6 cm

3. (a) Your drawing will be right if the sides are
   about 6 cm, 6 cm and 3·7 cm

   (b) 15·7 m

Angles

1.

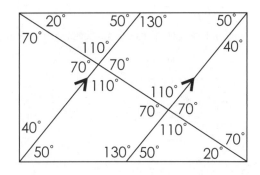

2. (a)

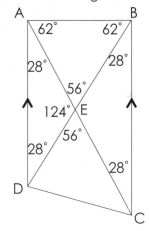

   (b) Triangle ACE is isosceles (base angles
   equal) so two sides the same.

   (c) Both the same (which you proved
   above).

3. If we assume AEB IS isosceles and fill in
   angles we seem to get

A 62° 62° B
28° 28°
56°
124° E
56°
28° 28°
D
C

ADE and BEC are isosceles also ... making

AE = ED = EB, which is impossible.

3. Maps and plans

1. (a) 68 km

   (b) 1 cm represents 15 km.

2. (a) (i) 162°

   (ii) 233°

   (b) (i) 37 km

   (ii) 35 km

3. 292°

4. Coordinates

1. (a)

[coordinate graph with points A, B, C, D, E, F, G, H plotted]

   (b) D(8, 6)

   (c) (4, 5·5)

   (d) E(4, 3), F(10, 7), G(12, 4), H(6, 0)

2. (a)

centre (5, 6)

(b) 10 m

5. Symmetry

1. (a)

(b) 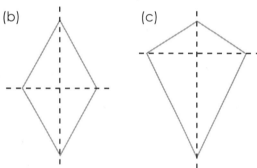   (c)

2. (a)

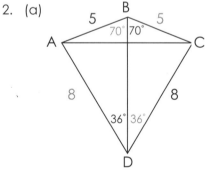

(b) (i) 140°, 72°, 74°, 74°

(ii) 26 cm

3. The word 'REFLECTED'

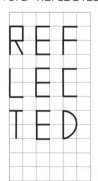

INFORMATION HANDLING

1. Data handling

1. (a) 6·6 cm

(b) 2·6 sec

2. (a) (i) yellow

(ii) red

(b)

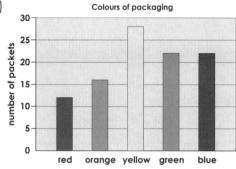

(c) 100 packets

(d) $\frac{16}{100} = \frac{4}{25}$

3. (a)

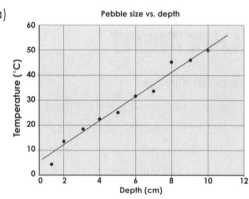

(b) the greater the depth, the greater the pebble size.

2. Probability

1. (a) 0

(b) 1

2. (a) (i) $\frac{kings\ left}{cards\ left} = \frac{3}{45} = \frac{1}{15}$

(ii) $\frac{sixes\ left}{cards\ left} = \frac{4}{45}$

(b) 1 heart gone, 3 spades gone so (i) is more likely.

3. (a) min 9°C; max 17°C

(b) 13°C

(c) $\frac{5}{12}$